KING BRUNO

KING BRUNO

a true story

written and illustrated by PAUL GLYNN

TO MY PARENTS, MICHAEL AND MARIE

With special thanks to:
Bala, Frankie and all the staff at Tacugama, Jane Goodall, Sally Biasiutti, Andreas Thiesen, Hannah Pearson, Fearghal O'Nuallain, Neil Cummins, Rebecca Williams, Greg Pittard, Katharine Smith, Frances Corcoran, Stephen O'Brien, Matt Harlock, Aminatta Forna and Stephanie Farrimond

Text and illustrations © Paul Glynn 2013
First published 2013 by Gola Books, 38 Hollingbourne Road, London SE24 9ND

Printed and bound in Great Britain by York Publishing Services

The right of Paul Glynn to be identified as the author of this work has been asserted in accordance with the Copyright, Designs and Patents Act 1988.

A CIP catalogue record for this book is available from the British Library

ISBN 978-0-9575269-0-7

Sierra Leone

Sierra Leone lies between Guinea and Liberia on the coast of West Africa. Fertile and rich in mineral wealth, it is home to over five million people and a diverse range of wildlife, from forest elephants and lions to pygmy hippos. Six thousand Western Chimpanzees live in Sierra Leone - the second largest population in West Africa. Between 1991 and 2002 civil war devastated Sierra Leone and displaced many of its inhabitants. Since then the country has made a steady recovery, with refugees and members of the diaspora returning home.

Foreword

Chimpanzees are more like us than any other animal, in biology and behaviour. They kiss, embrace, pat one another on the back, make and use tools. They can be violent and aggressive, but - like us - also show love, compassion and altruism. They have emotions similar to those we call happiness and sadness, fear and despair. They show anger, frustration, and grief when a close family member or friend dies. They have a sense of humour, and a sense of self.

I met Bruno in Sierra Leone in the early 1990s: a juvenile chimpanzee who had been rescued from a street vendor by Bala Amarasekaran and his wife Sharmila. I had left the forest paradise of Gombe National Park, where I had been studying chimpanzees in the wild since 1960, to see the plight of chimpanzees elsewhere in Africa, where they are threatened by habitat loss and poaching.

We took Bruno and Julie in a car to enjoy a walk in the forest. I remember talking to Bala about the need for a sanctuary for all the orphan chimpanzees in Sierra Leone. Such an undertaking involves a huge commitment: chimpanzees are strong, intelligent and can live for more than sixty years. It was a challenge Bala decided to take on.

This book is a marvellous testament to the determination, commitment and courage of Bala, Sharmila and their staff, who have worked so hard to ensure that Bruno and his friends have the best possible life. The illustrations are brilliant, capturing the essence and personality of the different chimpanzees and the forest surrounding their home. Beautifully written by Paul Glynn, *King Bruno* is enchanting, moving and educational, and will appeal to young and old alike.

Jane Goodall, PhD, DBE
Founder - the Jane Goodall Institute &
UN Messenger of Peace
www.janegoodall.org

Prologue

Where is Bruno? Ask the people of Sierra Leone, and they will tell you. Some say Bruno is in the Gola forest, leading his troops; others say he is dead, shot by a madman who wanted his blood. Schoolboys laugh and sing songs about Bruno; mothers warn their children not to wander in the jungle in case they meet him. Somewhere in the last stands of forest, in the wild backwoods, Bruno lives on: a spirit from a younger earth.

The story of his life is well known among local people. But it was his escape from captivity, on April 23rd 2006, which brought Bruno to international attention. He was quickly blamed for the tragedy, which left one man dead and another seriously injured. In the chaos that followed, Bruno vanished into the jungle.

Since then, a handful of sightings have been reported, while an alleged photograph of Bruno, taken in 2009, has never been verified. Countless searches of the Western Area Forest Reserve have turned up nothing and, at the time of writing, Bruno remains at large.

Rumours about what really happened that day continue to circulate, and every year the legend grows. But it seems that Bruno's whereabouts, like the reasons for his disappearance, will remain a mystery.

The Forest

They were coming. Down by the stream, a stork pulled itself up from the mud bank and took to the sky. An antelope raised its head, ears twitching. Bruno dropped the stick he was playing with and looked up. He was nine months old, the youngest chimpanzee in his group. He could barely climb a tree, and still depended on his mother's milk. But he knew the hum of the forest. It was like music to him, and when he heard it change he squealed in excitement.

There was a cry from the canopy. It was Gombe, the biggest of the males, powerful enough to tackle a young leopard, and at the sound of his call Bruno's mother scooped her son into her arms. All around, the trees swayed and crashed as the chimps fled. They were coming. Bruno could smell them – a dry, smoky smell, like burnt wood. Nothing like a chimp. They had been coming since the end of the rains, and no one knew what they were, or even if they were dangerous. But Gombe was afraid, and every time he saw them, he sounded the alarm.

Bruno and his mother were high in the trees now, swinging from branch to branch, and around him the world spun. Bruno loved the feeling in his stomach, the wind in his fur. It was like flying. They reached the boughs of a cotton tree, and then she stopped and kissed him. He felt her heartbeat quicken as she turned around. She wanted to see them.

Bruno wriggled in excitement. They were close. No-one had ever been this close. He could hear them stumbling about down below, sending flurries of birds into the sky, and he watched as the undergrowth shook and they emerged.

Bruno let out a squawk. He had seen many things in his short life in the forest. He had watched a python swallow a bushbuck without chewing. He had seen a chameleon change colour and vanish into the leaves. But he had never seen creatures like these.

They were *chimps*. Tall, upright chimps with skinny arms and smooth skin. They chattered to one another as they picked their way across the forest, stopping wherever the creepers and ferns grew too thick. They didn't use their arms to swing through the trees. They didn't like the forest at all. Every rustle made them flinch, as though the jungle might suddenly come alive and eat them.

Only when they looked up did he see their faces. A chimp's face was deep and proud, with splendid jaws and a jutting brow. But these creatures had flat faces. Their skin was shiny, like a snake's, and their eyes bulged. They weren't chimps at all.

Bruno buried his face in his mother's fur. Her heart was pounding now. She rose and reached for the nearest branch, and as she did so, one of the creatures raised a stick to its shoulder. It was a strange stick, black and shiny, and he pointed it carefully at her. There was a flash, a puff of smoke, a crack like two stones smashing together.

Something hit her. Bruno did not see it but he felt her body shake. Her hand stopped in mid-air, grasping at nothing. Then she fell. Bruno held on and screamed. They plunged through the canopy, branches snapping and chimps howling around them, and down below, the two creatures rushed forward, mouths open and flat teeth glinting in hideous grins.

A Voice In the Trees

He was born at the end of the rainy season, when the rivers run full and the air is sweet and clear and the forest hums with life. Frogs burped, birds squawked and chattered, termites marched across the forest floor. Young chimps wrestled and tumbled and practised building nests. Their parents watched over them. From time to time, they would hear the hiss of a snake or the silky footsteps of a leopard. The alarm cry would sound, and mothers would gather their babies and flee into the trees.

It was during these early months that Bruno first noticed the sound. Around him, trees creaked and buckled in the breeze. Insects hummed, a million wings beating together. But beneath them all was something else; a slow rise and fall like the breathing of some enormous animal. Bruno nuzzled close to his mother, and she cocked her head and listened. She could hear it too. The forest whispered, and although his mother fell still, Bruno could see that she was not afraid.

There were other dangers in the forest. One day, as Bruno and his mother foraged

in a clearing, a shape appeared in the trees above them. In an instant, Gombe was up, calling. As the chimps panicked and fled, figures dropped from the canopy; monsters with black fur and yellow teeth and blazing eyes.

The attack was brief. Later that day, the survivors found each other at the far end of the valley. One of the group was missing – an old male – and when Gombe called to him, a strange cry answered. Bruno heard it, and he knew that the creatures that had attacked them were not leopards or lions. They were rival chimps, looking to claim new territory, and now their cries rose and fell in a raw chant of victory.

But even this could not explain the sound in the trees. It wasn't a forest buffalo or a hippopotamus, or even an elephant, and although he had never seen it, Bruno sensed it was more powerful than any of them. When the sun fell and the sky flowered in red and yellow, the chimps would stop and watch. At times like this Bruno felt it draw close; a great heart beating in the gloom, and he longed to look for its source.

He never got his chance. When he was nine months old the humans came, and at the sound of their footsteps the forest fell silent. The humans raised their black stick and his mother fell to the ground, and after that his eyes went black and he remembered nothing.

When Bruno woke, it was cold. He shivered and pawed the dirt. The beating of her heart was gone. She had never left him, not for more than a few seconds. He mewled and opened his eyes. A bird circled in the sky, drawing closer with each turn, its black feathers shimmering in the sun. A hooded vulture; a bird that lived off the dead and dying.

Bruno sat up. He had been tied to a tree. The hum of the forest was gone. The air was heavy with smoke and the stench of roasted meat, and out of the dust rose great structures, like termite mounds topped with sheaves of yellow grass.

Where was she? She had fallen from the tree but he had held on tight. She couldn't be far…

Bruno screamed. There were humans everywhere, milling and chattering, carrying things on their heads. He scrambled behind the tree, and they looked at him and laughed. Bruno knew what laughter was – it was a sound you made when another chimp tickled you or when you found a good stick to play with. But this was different. It was loud and harsh; the laugh of someone pleased with their own power.

He could see now just how similar to chimps they were. They had chimp eyes and chimp hands and carried their young on their backs, just as a chimp would. Nearby, a pair of females were digging the ground with sticks. So they could use tools, too, just like chimps.

As Bruno watched, a group of male humans appeared, and when the females heard them they chattered and touched each other's hands. The males carried a long branch between them. Hanging from it, its head trailing and its brown coat flecked with blood, was a bushbuck – a splendid forest antelope. Bruno watched as the carcass was lowered. He had seen Gombe and his friends hunt – catching small antelope and colobus monkeys to share among the group. It was nothing like this.

That night, the humans lit fires and gathered around them. They were not afraid of fire. They loved its light and warmth as a plant loves the sun, and as Bruno watched them he shivered and cried to be picked up. Above him, in the trees, the vultures waited.

Days passed. There was no one to hug, no milk to drink, and as Bruno got colder and hungrier, his hair fell out and he slept more and more. He dreamt of his mother; of playing in the grass on lazy afternoons - riding on her back, his face buried in her warm thick fur.

As he dreamed there was a beat of wings, and the vultures called. He rolled over. He was still in the forest. His mother ran her fingers through his fur and scratched his ears. Then she cupped his face and he squirmed. Her skin was wrong – hairless and damp and horrible. He opened his eyes.

A human male crouched over him. He wore something on his head to shield his eyes from the sun, and there was a tuft of fur on his chin. Bruno scrambled to his feet. The man was sad. Bruno could tell by the shape of his mouth and the softness in his eyes. He looked at Bruno, and as the sadness deepened a woman appeared beside him. Then the man rose and began to chatter to the villagers. There was something in his hands. It looked like a small sheaf of leaves. Both the strange man and the villagers treated these leaves with great respect, and everyone watched as he counted them out and handed them over. All the time he chattered, pointing to Bruno and shaking his head.

The woman reached out and stroked Bruno. She smelled of milk and flowers, and when he felt the warmth of her hand, he crawled towards her. She picked him up. Bruno felt the steady thump inside her chest and he pressed against her.

The villagers crowded round. There were faces and voices, eyes and teeth flashing, yelps and shrieks and reaching hands. She shielded him with her arm and placed him inside something enormous and foul-smelling. Then the earth began to move.

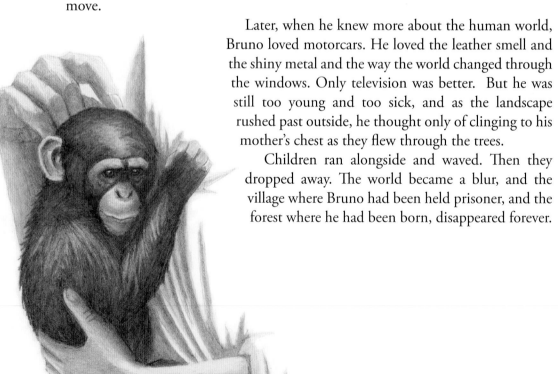

Later, when he knew more about the human world, Bruno loved motorcars. He loved the leather smell and the shiny metal and the way the world changed through the windows. Only television was better. But he was still too young and too sick, and as the landscape rushed past outside, he thought only of clinging to his mother's chest as they flew through the trees.

Children ran alongside and waved. Then they dropped away. The world became a blur, and the village where Bruno had been held prisoner, and the forest where he had been born, disappeared forever.

The Human Kingdom

Bruno. That was the sound the two humans made when they looked at him. Sometimes they whispered it, sometimes they shouted, sometimes they hissed or growled. But it was always the same. They even had sounds for each other: *Bala* was the man and *Sharmila* was the woman. They had hundreds of sounds, so many that Bruno could not keep track, and they spent all their time chattering like birds.

It was confusing. Chimps use their bodies to talk. A grunt or a hoot can mean something different when a chimp is showing his teeth, or when he is throwing out his hands, or moving his eyes, or putting things in his mouth.

Bala and Sharmila did this too, but in their own strange way. Sharmila would raise her eyebrows at Bala to show she was serious, and Bala's shoulders went stiff if he was unhappy. All Bruno knew was that he was *Bruno*.

He had learned a great deal about humans while he was held prisoner in the village. He had seen men building huts to live in. He had watched women grooming each other's hair and using tools to prepare food for their husbands. Bruno could already sense that humans valued their families: that fathers and mothers and aunts and uncles were important to humans, just as they are to chimps.

He could not know that Bala's father lived in a town in the provinces of Sierra Leone, and that Bala and Sharmila had been travelling to visit him when they heard about a baby chimp being kept alive in a nearby village. When they saw Bruno huddled under a tree, they knew they could not leave him to die. And so they had bought him, and taken him to their home in the city.

Bruno wasn't the only animal in the house. As soon as his strength returned he began to explore, and it wasn't long before he met Sheba. She licked his nose and he stroked her fur and smelled his fingers. A dog. The big ones were dangerous. Sharmila picked Sheba up and cuddled her, and when Bruno saw this he slapped the ground and started to cry. Sharmila put Sheba down and picked Bruno up instead.

He soon realised that Sharmila would not hurt him. Every day she brought him hot, delicious food. Bruno's fur grew back and he began to climb and swing, thrilled with his new home. There was only one problem: Bala.

If Sharmila was a female, Bruno didn't know what Bala was. He was certainly nothing like a male chimp. He was a fussy, fragile creature who never shouted or threw anything or jumped about. Instead, he hung around, interfering. Bruno hated him. When Bala was with Sharmila, he would smile at her and touch her shoulder and her voice would grow warm. When Bruno screamed and drove him away, she would put him down and refuse to play. The ground was cold and Bruno cried and cried.

Everything in Bala and Sharmila's house was dead. There were no birds, no sky. No stink of moss or fruit. But there were no snakes either; no leopards or scorpions. Strange objects hung everywhere, glittering like wet stones. Clocks, glasses, pictures in frames. Bruno touched them and sniffed his fingers but they smelled of nothing. They made him dizzy, made him jump and laugh and slap himself. As soon as he was strong enough, he picked up one of these toys and threw it and it shattered. The noise was good. No stick or stone made a sound like that. He smashed another one and laughed. Then a pair of legs appeared and Bala's voice boomed.

Bruno screamed for Sharmila. When Bala's

hands closed around him, he turned and bit him. He wriggled free and lunged for the curtains but he was getting heavier, and there was a loud rip as they came free and Bruno tumbled in a pile onto the floor.

Bala stood over Bruno and stroked the tuft of fur on his chin. Then he picked him up and took him out to the car.

Outside the house, buildings towered in the sky like mountains and Bruno squealed and jumped up and down. There were humans all over the place. He called for Sharmila, and as the city passed and the forest appeared, he climbed over the seats, searching for a way out. Bala said nothing. He turned the car in among the tall trees, climbing a bumpy dirt track until the road was hidden. Here he stopped.

Bruno panted. He didn't want to go back to the forest. All he remembered was his mother, lying fallen on the ground. Bala got out and opened the door and the damp air of the forest rushed in. Bruno's chest grew tight. He scrambled back across the seat and crouched down. There was the smell of rotten leaves, the chirp of insects, the sigh of swaying branches. And beyond all that, deep in the trees, was something else: a deep rise and fall, like the breathing of some mighty creature.

He began to screech and thrash, and Bala looked down sternly at him. He grabbed Bruno by the waist and pulled. Bruno held on as long as he could. Then he let go and jumped onto Bala's foot, wrapping his arms tightly around his leg. Bala sighed and shook his head, and together they limped off into the forest.

Not far away lay a clearing where dry leaves rustled on the ground. Through a gap in the trees, a green lake shimmered. Once, Bruno would have been happy to stop at a place like this, to sleep and play in the grass. Now he held on to Bala and whimpered.

Bala's stride became slower and his eyes wandered into the canopy. He stopped and sat down, and one by one he peeled away Bruno's hands and feet. Then he carried him to the nearest tree and placed him in it.

Bruno scrabbled. He was still a poor climber. He managed to catch a branch in one hand but it was too thin, and before he could grab hold of it with his feet, it began to bend. He dangled in the air, spinning in panic.

Just when he was sure to fall, a pair of warm hands caught Bruno under his arms. They held him steady until he found a better branch, and as he pulled himself up, Bala smiled. His voice was soft and husky, like a breeze in dry grass. Bruno

grunted and climbed onto Bala's head, clinging to the curly hair that sprouted from the top. When Bruno had tired of climbing, Bala took out a box of mango and banana, and when Bruno crawled eagerly into his lap, Bala tickled him until he squirmed and snorted.

The shadows grew long, and Bala picked him up. Bruno felt the soft thump of his heart. They were going home. Back to Sharmila and Sheba, to a human house with warmth and light and food. They drove away from the forest, and as the sun fell, the city appeared below them and the hills lit up like a starlit sky.

Learning the Ropes

Back in the forest, all the young chimps had wanted to be like Gombe. They staggered around with twigs and leaves, trying to impress one another. Their mothers showed them how to use stones and sticks to crack nuts or scoop honey out of a bee's nest. Fishing for termites was the hardest. First you chose a twig and stripped it of its leaves. Then the twig went into a hole in the side of a termite mound. Once the twig was covered in termites, you drew it out and ate them. The twigs had to be perfect – not too short and not too wide. And the termites didn't like being caught. When Bruno took his first delicious mouthful, they bit his tongue and he yelped.

But all this was easy compared to living with Bala. Swinging was banned in the house, and so was breaking. Every morning, while Sharmila combed her hair, Bala proudly buttoned his clean white shirt to the neck. Bruno studied them. He ran his fingers through his own fur and played with the buttons. He wanted to be a human, clean and dainty. And so, when he turned around one day and saw the neat, perfect poo he had left on the carpet, Bruno grunted anxiously.

In the forest, no-one would have minded. In the forest you went to the toilet anywhere, as long as it wasn't in your own nest. You could even pick your poo up and throw it around.

Bruno had lived in Bala and Sharmila's house for nearly a year now, and he had never once seen Bala throw his own poo around. He never fought or slapped or bit Sharmila, and when he ate, he held back his farts and grunts. In all this time, the only other chimps Bruno had seen were in the TV, where they couldn't get out and hurt him. These strange chimps had houses of their own, with ropes and tyres to play on, and although Bala studied them with interest, Bruno was relieved when the TV was off and they went away. That was all finished now. Bala and Sharmila loved him. He wanted to stay with them, in their house full of toys, far away from the forest. That was why he was concerned about the poo.

Bruno fidgeted. He had to do something about it before Bala returned home. Then he remembered. Upstairs, in a small room, stood a bowl with a puddle of water and a roll of paper beside it. This was where Bala and Sharmila made their toilet. It had taken Bruno months to find it.

He panted in excitement, dashed up the stairs and grabbed the paper. Then he stopped. There were toys everywhere – a fuzzy white stick for cleaning your teeth, a comb for grooming. Bruno couldn't resist. He dropped the toothbrush in the toilet bowl and pressed the handle. He laughed as the brush spun round and round and disappeared. Then he stopped. Bala would never do this. Bala would finish the job he had begun. Bruno ran downstairs and set to work.

It was harder than it looked. The roll of toilet paper was big and Bruno's hands were small. When he wiped at his poo, it just seemed to spread everywhere. But in the end it was gone. The carpet was brown and sticky and piles of brown paper lay everywhere. Bruno clapped and jumped up and down. Bala would be happy.

Bala wasn't happy. When he walked through the door and saw the mess on the floor, he stared at Bruno as though something invisible had hit him on the head. Then he picked Bruno up and took him outside. Bruno squirmed. When they reached the garden, he screamed and rolled around. He pooed again and threw his poo at the neighbour's car. Then he climbed the mango tree.

It stood at the end of the garden, and it was the one place where Bruno was free to do what he wanted. Bala never followed him. Bruno's feet and hands were clever – they found the branches without looking. But Bala was slow, and the more Bruno barked at him, the slower he got.

Outside Bala and Sharmila's garden lay the city. Humans crowded the streets, chattering, carrying piles of wood or fruit or toys. Bruno sat on a branch and watched. They were like chimps in so many ways. He had seen them hug and kiss each other and sit close to teach things to their young ones. They were clumsy and had no sense of humour, but they were also patient. They weren't afraid of the dark or the forest; they didn't need the sun or rain or plants or animals. They built their own world - a world without shadows or strange noises, a world that was safe and comfortable - and Bruno longed to be like them.

He was in the tree again when Bala called him. Bruno heard the warm ring in his voice and swung down, panting happily. As he reached the ground, a small hairy figure stepped out from behind Bala's leg. She had been playing with the laces of Bala's shoe, but when she looked up and saw Bruno, she opened her arms.

"Bruno," Bala said, "this is Julie."

Bruno stopped. Julie was a chimp. A young chimp, not much older than him. Bala smiled at Julie and handed her a piece of banana. Bruno's throat choked up. She was in his house. Eating his food. Playing with Bala's shoe. Bruno trembled. Then he screamed and charged.

She was too quick, and as Bala yelled at Bruno, Julie slipped away, across the garden and into the branches of the mango tree. Bruno scooped up a stone and threw it. Julie laughed. He swung into the tree after her. *No.* Bala was his.

Julie leapt from the tree to the roof. She was still laughing, like this was all a game. Bruno barked, but when he had her cornered, Julie jumped from the roof to the wall at the edge of Bala's garden.

She was running along the top of this wall when suddenly she stumbled and screamed. Now he would show her. She had slipped and cut her hand. She wasn't laughing anymore. Her eyes were frightened and she whimpered as Bruno grabbed her and Bala yelled.

It was then that he smelled her. It was a forgotten smell, musty and warm, and suddenly Bruno stopped. He swayed. Then he wrapped his arms around her and pressed his nose into her fur, breathing deeply. Julie kissed him and, from the ground below, Bala gave an approving shout.

After that, it was useless. Julie was here to stay. If Bruno beat her or bit her, or stole her dinner, Bala would scold him and lock him in the cage he had built in the garden. Bruno howled and rolled around, tearing out clumps of his own fur. But the weeks passed, and Bala did not budge.

Julie was better than Bruno at everything. She knew how to comb her fur and paint her face, just like Sharmila. When they slept in the bed, she arranged the sheets, straightening them until they were perfect. She could pluck fruit from the trees in the back garden with a long stick, just like Bala, and when they went on forest walks, she scampered fearlessly amongst the snakes and bugs while Bruno hid in the car. He sulked and threw stones at her.

She must have seen him playing with Sheba, because one day Julie came to Bruno in the garden and nudged him. He snorted and got up. Then he stopped. In her hands, she held a puppy. Soft and yellow and warm. Bruno took it and ran his fingertips through its fur. Then he kissed it and Julie clapped. She disappeared for a moment and when she returned, she had a puppy of her own. Together they climbed into the mango tree. Below them, Sheba appeared, searching for her missing babies.

At the top of the tree, Julie sat down on a branch. With her puppy in one hand, she began to twist and bend the branches.

At first, Bruno didn't understand. Then a memory came to him. He was in the forest, in his mother's arms. As night fell the trees whispered, and all the animals scurried and hid, as though a living thing had come to hunt them. Snakes and lizards fell still as the air grew cold. Birds hurried to roost. Through the gloom, Bruno's mother broke and bent branches and twisted them together, her lip drooped in concentration. She was building a nest for them; a bed to sleep in. When it was finished, she would line it with leaves and they would lie down together…

Bruno blinked, and the memory was gone. Julie took the two puppies and placed them in the nest she had built, panting happily as they mewled and crawled around. Down below them, Sheba began to howl. Bala appeared, to see what the fuss was about. When he saw the puppies in the tree, he shook his head. Then he started to climb. He placed one foot gingerly on the first branch and groped for the next one.

Julie watched him and laughed. It was a soft chimp laugh; a laugh that started in her throat and spread down to her belly until her whole body shook. When Bruno heard it and saw Bala, he laughed too.

Then Julie turned and began to groom Bruno. Her fingers ran through his fur, checking it was straight and clean and free of dirt. It felt nice. Bruno turned to groom her back, and as he heard her grunt of contentment, he knew at last he had found a friend.

Partners in Crime

It was dry in the city. There were no trees shrouded in mist, no clouds drifting on the hills. The mud and damp of the forest had been driven away, and Bruno was glad. He loved the smoky smell of the human world, with its sweat and oil and rumbling motorcars. Every time Bala took them to the forest, Bruno saw that the humans had advanced, clearing the trees ahead of them, and he knew that one day they would cover the whole world.

He had grown quickly, and as he began his fifth year in Bala and Sharmila's house, Bruno brimmed with strength. He knew Bala's rules now, and knew he was supposed to follow them. But there were other, more important rules: who was strongest, who deserved respect, who was a friend and who was an enemy.

Back in the forest, Gombe was leader. If he wanted a mango or a piece of meat, whoever was closest to it gave way and let him have it. Gombe wasn't just strong – he was smart. He could impress his rivals by puffing up his fur and shaking branches and throwing stones. His displays were brilliant and scary and he had friends to back him up. He rarely needed to fight.

Humans had their own system, and Bruno studied it. He watched them from the mango tree in the garden, or through the car window when Bala took him outside. He saw that humans never fought or killed one another. Each one knew its place. The strongest had big houses and colourful clothes, while the weakest lay by the side of the road, arms outstretched in hunger and submission. When these weak people rapped on a car window, the driver would scowl and look away. If they followed a fat woman down the street, she would shout and wave them off with her hands. There was nothing the weak people could do. They had no cars, no toys. They were powerless.

This was the order which Bruno saw, and he longed to be part of it. He had the sunglasses and trainers and caps Bala had given to him. When Bruno swaggered on his back legs and bared his teeth, strangers shrank away and flapped their hands. He barked and hooted. He was strong and important, and no-one could touch him.

Bruno was sitting at his usual place in the mango tree one afternoon when something struck the back of his head. He yelped and turned. A young man stood on the other side of the wall. Bruno had seen him before – he worked as a carpenter for Bala's neighbour. As Bruno watched, the carpenter picked up another stone and threw it. Bruno jumped aside. The carpenter laughed. Bruno barked again and shimmied down the tree, calling for Bala.

The carpenter came many times. He seemed to think Bruno and Julie were dogs or chickens. Bruno would show him. He bristled at the thought of beating the carpenter, and waited for his chance. But one day Bala came and spoke to the carpenter, and after that the stones and the visits stopped.

Frustrating as this was, things soon got worse for Bruno and Julie. Bala began to keep them in their cage all the time.

It happened after a walk in the hills outside the city. For hours they wrestled in the grass, and Bruno scratched Bala's head and panted with laughter as Bala's hands found his armpits. When they drove home, Bruno sat in the front seat beside Bala as people stared and pointed.

They had just reached the city when the sound of the engine changed. Bala frowned. There was a sputter, and the car rolled to a halt. Julie grunted anxiously. Bala got out. He opened up the front of the car and, as he shook his head, strangers began to gather round.

Bruno watched the strange humans and panted. His chest was tight. Faces loomed in the windows. *No.* They had their hands on the car. He gibbered and slapped the seats.

From far away came Bala's voice, trying to comfort him. Bruno rocked and bounced and then something broke in him and he roared. His fists flew. The strangers jumped back. *Yes.* With a howl, Bruno punched the windshield, and it shattered into a thousand pieces.

They drove home with the breeze in their faces. Bala was quiet. He didn't understand. Bruno had shown the strangers who was stronger. But Bala got upset about these things, and when he took Bruno to his cage, he hugged him and said he loved him. Then he climbed out and locked the door.

After that, they were stuck inside. It was boring. Bruno and Julie pushed twigs into the lock to see if it would open. Then one morning, Bruno grabbed the bars and pressed his feet against the cage wall. He could feel his own strength, aching to get out. He pulled. The bars creaked. Julie hooted and clapped. This was good. The cage was weak. Bruno's muscles burned but he didn't stop, bracing himself as the bars began to bend, until he had made a gap wide enough for them to climb through.

They raced along the garden wall. From the neighbour's garden came a squawk and a flap of wings. Bruno and Julie swung down with hoots of excitement.

A few moments later, Bruno stood in a cloud of dust and feathers and stared at the chicken at his feet. He stroked it with his fingertips. He had thrown it at the wall and now it wouldn't get up. The other chickens were still running and flapping. Then Julie barked. She had found the eggs.

Bruno forgot the dead chicken and climbed onto the wall. From there he reached the tree and sprang to the roof. Once Bala arrived, the game could really begin. He was frightened of the roof, and it was fun to sit on the edge and laugh at him.

An engine rumbled and there was a clatter of metal as the gates were opened. Bala appeared. Someone was with him; a familiar figure, and when he spoke, Bruno bristled. It was him. The carpenter. He smiled and chattered to Bala, and Bala nodded as he led him inside. Bruno spat out his eggshell and climbed down.

He was in the hallway, gathering himself to attack, when he felt it. A heavy feeling, deep in his chest. Bala would know. Bala always knew when Bruno broke things; he knew when he robbed food from the fridge. He always knew it was Bruno, even when he hadn't seen him. Bruno could imagine his scowl, hear the rumble in his voice. He wilted as the heavy feeling got worse. Then he shook himself. No. The carpenter had challenged him, and he was strong. He hovered in the hallway, just out of view. Then he snapped and ran.

When the carpenter saw a half-grown chimp charging at him with its teeth bared and fur raised, he let out a cry of horror. Bruno dashed past Bala and sank his teeth into the man's leg until he tasted blood. Then he turned and ran.

It wasn't a serious bite. Bruno had bitten Julie just as hard many times. But Julie was a chimp, with thick chimp skin, and when Bala caught him Bruno cowered and put his hands over his head. He could understand Bala's words now, and this time he scolded Bruno as never before.

"That's it, Bruno," Bala growled. "I'm finished with you. Do you understand? I don't want to see you anymore."

Bala waved his arms. Bruno knew it wasn't true. The carpenter had deserved his punishment and Bala knew it. But the words stung worse than any beating.

When Bala picked Bruno up and carried him to the cage, he knew better than to escape again. His rage exploded, and he bounded around and beat his hands on himself and the bars and the cement floor. When he was spent he sat sullenly, until Julie came and hugged him.

After that, the cage was repaired and they were kept inside. At times, Sharmila would sit outside with Bala and talk to Bruno and Julie through the bars. When she said Bruno's name, Bala's eyes grew soft and confused. Something had changed in her. Her mouth was set, and Bruno looked at her hopefully. They had escaped the cage once, so what was the point of returning? Maybe they could live in the house again.

Then one night, the door opened. Bruno groaned and rolled over. Julie yawned. It wasn't even light. Bala stood at the gate and when he dragged them out, they stumbled through the garden into a second cage with wheels on the bottom. The door slammed, and they began to move.

The breeze whistled over them, and down below the city twinkled as they drove into the hills. Bruno was awake now. Where were they going? They never went for walks this early. The lights of the city vanished behind a wall of jungle and Bruno bared his teeth. They were at that place; the place where Bala had first taken him years ago, where the trees stood tall and silent and a lake rippled in the twilight. And in the centre of the clearing stood an empty cage.

It was bigger and stronger than the cage in Bala's yard. Through the bars, Bruno saw piles of food. Sweets and biscuits. Fresh bananas and mangoes. Julie perked up. When the gate opened, she scampered inside and rummaged through the treasure. Bala turned.

"It's okay, Bruno. Go ahead."

Bruno looked up at the dark trees and shivered. He didn't move. Julie called him and he gripped the bars. Bala scratched his beard. Then he vanished, and when he reappeared, he held something white in his hands. Shoes. White, clean shoes with

neat laces. The kind he used to wear when Bruno rode around on his foot. They smelled of a nice house and sheets to sleep on and toys to play with. Bruno let go of the bars and swayed. Bala placed the shoes beside Julie, and when she saw them, she gave a grunt of delight and picked one up. It was more than Bruno could bear. He hurried into the cage and snatched the shoe from Julie.

Behind him the door clanged shut. Something burst inside him. He hurled himself at the bars and reached for Bala. *No.* Bruno heaved, a sob aching in his throat. He would not be left alone in the forest, not again. He shook and rattled the bars. *No!*

Bruno screamed and rolled around as Bala tried to console him. The forest was safe. He could hear it in Bala's voice. Bala stroked Bruno's fingers through the bars, and when he rose his eyes were wet. Bruno howled. Then Bala got into his car and started the engine, and Bruno was alone with Julie and the sounds of the wilderness.

Sanctuary

They came from all over the country. Some arrived in a cage in the back of Bala's car; others were brought by strangers who hugged and cuddled them as they said goodbye.

Confused as they were, they knew a great deal about humans: Tito spent all his time sweeping the floor, while Christo could hammer nails and pour water from a tap. Augusta was crazy, her eyes staring and her body criss-crossed with scars; Littleboy was a thief and a trickster who could snatch a radio or a pot of rice with a moment's distraction. Bigger than all of them were Phillip and Charlie; a pair of sturdy males who quickly became best friends.

Each new arrival was taken to a clearing in the hills, and as they arrived a cry would rise; a chorus of screams and whoops and rattling bars. They would stare at their new home: the cages, the cleaners and chimps. Then they were taken inside. Here, the humans bathed them and treated their wounds until at last, after a meal of bananas and milk, they were ready to meet their new family.

It was years since any of them had smelled or touched another chimp, and for a moment they gazed at each other. Then they hugged and rolled in the leaves. Some were so excited that they refused to let go of their new playmates. From her cage, Julie watched them, and as she stretched her arm between the bars they ran to her and rolled and laughed as she tickled them.

At the other end of Julie's cage sat a chimp that no-one dared approach. He was enormous - bigger than Phillip and Charlie put together. His fur was black and glossy, and when he was angry it would stand on end and ripple, as though touched by an electric current. His rages were terrifying. When men came to clean his cage, he snatched their brooms and buckets, and as they fled he pounded the bars with his fists.

During his worst tantrums, Bala would appear.

"Bruno boy!" he would shout. "How are you? Are you behaving?"

Bala would laugh, and Bruno would throw his arms through the bars, squeezing Bala until he could hardly breathe. They were friends, and one day Bala would take him away from this awful place, and they would live in the city again.

Bruno didn't know that it was Bala who had built the cages. He had built the clinic for sick chimps and found people to look after them. He had even begun to round up other orphans like Bruno and Julie, and bring them to the forest clearing. Here they would be well cared for, and maybe some day, when the forest was safe, Bala would go back to his job in the city and the chimps could go back to where they belonged.

In the meantime he would take care of them. The neat white shirts were gone - now Bala wore a cap on his head and brown trousers. He knew every chimp by name and hooted to them as though he were a chimp himself. Every one of them loved Bala, and clamoured for his attention.

As the cages filled, Bala began to bring visitors. The small ones wore matching clothes and whooped and called to Bruno or stared at him the way a lizard stares at a bug. When Bruno pelted them with stones, they squealed and ran. Phillip and Charlie laughed. Even Bala laughed sometimes. If Bruno ran out of stones, he pooed in his hand instead and threw it in people's faces. When Bala climbed onto the roof to fix the cage, Bruno and Julie tied his shoelaces together, and when he tumbled to the ground, the chimps laughed until they choked.

But when dusk fell, the fun stopped. The trees came to life with chirps and slithers, and Bruno shivered. From deep in the bush came the soft rise and fall of a living creature. He heard it only on the darkest nights, when the humans were gone and the lights of the city seemed far away, and he rolled and barked in his sleep.

Bruno knew that he was not the only one who was afraid. Every day, men came to the clearing with tools on their backs. They chopped trees and dug the earth until sweat streamed from their bodies. Always, Bala was among them, chattering and pointing as machines growled and tore.

Sometimes, as they worked, these men cocked their heads and listened. And sometimes, as the men worked and the radio beside them babbled, they would chatter anxiously, gesturing to one another and then to an unknown place deep in the forest. From beyond the hills came the rumble of thunder and the crackle of branches. Flashes of lightning lit up the sky, but no rain ever fell.

At dawn, the young chimps were taken outside for walks, to learn how to climb and build nests. Bruno was kept in his cage. He was glad, and as he chewed idly on a piece of grass one morning he heard Phillip and Charlie barking at him.

Bruno rose. Phillip was standing on his back legs, his lips pulled back to show his teeth. Bruno rocked and hooted. He jumped until his head hit the roof and then he spun and slapped the concrete and screamed. Julie hid at the back of the cage. Phillip roared. He shook the bars and kicked them with his feet. Bruno hurled a stone at him and threw his shoulders against the cage with a whoop.

When it was over, he felt better. Phillip mooned about, grooming Charlie. Bruno settled. Phillip was watching the trees now with interest, and as the branches swayed, he got up.

There was a cry. From across the clearing came Littleboy, scrambling as fast as his legs would carry him. He slipped between the bars of Bruno's cage and jumped into Julie's arms. In the nursery, the baby chimps clutched each other in terror.

The forest was moving. Up in the canopy, a bulky shape swung from branch to branch. The leaves rustled and crunched as it stopped, and there was a thump as a figure dropped to the ground. Then a hand parted the ferns, and a wrinkled face appeared.

Bruno pressed against the bars. A chimp. A strange, ragged chimp, alone in the forest. She limped forward. Her name was Congo, and when she saw the cages and the chimps, she showed her teeth in a grimace of fear. Bruno could smell her now, and he bristled. She was an outsider; a wild chimp from the world they had left behind. He stood up and called to Bala.

Congo crept forward. But when she saw the mounds of earth and shining steel the humans had left, she stopped and cried out in alarm. Bruno's chest grew tight and he rattled the bars hopelessly. Then Congo spun around. She slapped the ground and screeched, and with a final call she plunged back into the forest.

It was hours before the chimps settled. When Bala appeared, Bruno lunged at him and ripped off his shirt. *No*. He wanted to go back. He wanted to eat ice cream and watch TV and clean up after himself and arrange the bedsheets and never bite anyone again. Bala freed himself and scolded Bruno, and Bruno rolled on the cage floor, tearing off great clumps of his own fur.

Dusk fell and the night hummed. When dawn broke, the clearing was empty. No strangers came. No young chimps were released to play in the forest. The mist that gathered at night thinned and rose, and then Bruno saw Bala crouching outside their cage. He watched Bruno until he caught his eye.

"Bruno? Bruno, I'm coming inside".

On any other day these words would have sent Bruno clapping and jumping in excitement. But today he turned away. He could feel Bala's eyes on the back of his head. A moment later the gate creaked, and Bala's warm arm slid around his shoulders. Phillip and Charlie watched. There was a strange alertness in the air, like waiting for thunder. Then Bala rose and tried to lead Bruno outside. No. He wouldn't go. He lowered his head and coughed, and Bala patted his back and ran his fingers through his fur.

"Come on, Bruno," he whispered. "I want to show you something".

Julie shuffled aside as Bruno stepped through the door. The outside yawned around them. They passed through another gate and Bruno clutched Bala's leg and looked down. They weren't going home. They were going into the forest. Behind them, every chimp in the clearing clung to the bars and watched. Bruno coughed and squeezed Bala's hand. Great sobs shook his body. On all sides lay the bush: dark and twisty, full of shadows. Bala was pulling his fingers away now, trying to make him let go. Bruno looked up and begged, and then he saw it…

A post rose above the trees. Silver wires ran from either side of it, and they joined another post not far away, and then another. A fence. A fence built by humans. Bruno let go of Bala's hands. There were logs and ropes. Tyres hung and swayed in the breeze. An enormous house stood at the edge of the fence. And then Bruno saw that he wasn't in the forest at all. He was in a garden. A garden filled with trees, big enough for a hundred chimps to run and climb and tumble.

Bala grinned. Bruno spun around and scratched his head. Then he ran. He whooped and bristled as he jumped to the first branch, caught it and swung, rose and caught the next. The world spun. The leaves were sweet; branches swayed and crashed.

Julie and Littleboy were led from their cages and behind them came Phillip and Charlie. Bruno burst through the canopy. For a moment, he was in the sun and the world below was tiny.

"Bruno!"

With a whoop, Bruno tumbled, snatching, ripping branches, grabbing with his hands and feet until he found his grip and swung. With a final gasp, he landed on the ground.

Bala waited by the fence. His eyes shone. With a roar, Bruno buried his face in Bala's shoulder, and Bala laughed and wiped his eyes. Chimps crowded round them. Bruno wanted to burst, wanted to hug Bala and scratch his head and tickle him and hear his sounds. All he had wanted was a home, a place where they could live together and feel safe. And Bala had given him one.

44

The Leopard People

There was a time in every dry season when the sky turned yellow. Dust arrived on the wind, carried from faraway deserts. It settled on the leaves of trees and on the grass, hanging in the air. It mingled with the smoke that rose where the city ate into the forest, and it mingled with the dust that rose from the land that the humans had cleared.

During Bruno's first year as leader of the chimps at the sanctuary, the air was thicker still. Strange, acrid smoke drifted from somewhere inland, but when Bruno smelled it he took it as another sign of human work, and he was happy. From the top of the tallest tree in the enclosure, he could still see the city, glittering in the distance. He was too far away to see the humans themselves. He did not know that the weakest among them had grown hungry, and that as the years passed their hunger had turned to rage.

Bruno loved the treats that Bala still brought him - the sunglasses and shoes. He preferred to sleep indoors and wake in the morning with strong human walls around him. Many of the chimps knew how to build nests, but they dared not defy Bruno by sleeping outside. He was their leader, and no-one could fail to see the connection he had with Bala.

Bruno had just woken on the morning that Sharmila came. The den was full, warm bodies piled around him like blankets. Soon, the sun would be up and breakfast would be served. Then Bala would come. He would be eager to check on Gido, their newest family member.

For weeks, Bala had brought Gido to the bars of the den so that the other chimps could smell and touch him, and learn to accept him when he came to live in their enclosure. Phillip and Charlie were uncertain – they had seen Gido arrive in a shining motorcar, handed over by a powerful man. Gido was proud and intelligent, and he would sulk about his low rank.

Bruno yawned. The rules were simple, and Gido had learned quickly. Serious fighting and bullying were not allowed. Every chimp got its fair share at feeding time, and no little ones were to be robbed of their meal. Afternoons were spent grooming and foraging, far away from the silver wires, and outside of mealtimes no one went near the fence. There was a tap which Julie showed Gido how to use if he wanted water, and within a few days he had settled in.

Now and again, Congo came to visit. They would hear her first, calling in the hills, and although Bruno ignored her, Gido was instantly drawn. He sat at the fence and hooted, throwing her pieces of food, and Congo ate gratefully.

Bruno dozed and stroked Littleboy's fur. From outside came a familiar voice, and he rose and blew excited kisses through the bars. Sharmila smiled and touched his hand.

A change had taken place in her. At first, Bruno thought she was sick. Her smell was different, and she carried herself as though her body was something fragile and precious. She stepped close to the bars and Bala hovered anxiously by her side. Sharmila laughed. Bruno stroked her hair and studied the colour on her fingernails, tasting it with his lips. His stomach rumbled as he thought of breakfast. Then, as if in response, there came a rumble from outside. The air shook. There was a hum like the wings of a giant mosquito, and Bala and Sharmila turned to look.

A bank of cloud drifted over the city, and beneath these mountains of white, something gleamed in the sky. As it turned towards them, the sound rose. It wasn't an insect. It was a machine, as big as a house, steel cylinders strapped to its belly. It hurtled towards them and screamed overhead, and as a gust of wind tore through the trees, the chimps hugged each other and whimpered. Bala and Sharmila looked up as the machine disappeared inland. Then it happened.

From the forest came a cry of alarm. It was Congo, and as she turned and fled, there was a clap like thunder. Men began to run. The ground shuddered as the flying machine roared again and swung above them. The chimps scattered. They all knew the sound of gunfire, and they all knew what it meant. Bala looked up and the colour drained from his face. He looked at Bruno and at Sharmila. Then he took her by the arm and ran.

Bruno charged outside to the fence and ran up and down, his teeth bared. It was coming. Something worse than any storm, something that scattered humans as though they were birds or mice. He howled at Bala to come back.

Then it was upon them. Flashes lit up the sky. Engines roared. The chimps scattered and hid in the trees, and when Bruno had climbed to the tallest branch, he turned and looked out towards the city.

It was burning. In places, whole buildings had been swallowed by flame, and smoke flowed into the sky like blood from a wound. Closer by, a road cut through the forest, and along this road, humans moved. They were spindly shapes, like black ants, trudging on foot or piled into motorcars. As they rounded the flank of the hill and saw the city in flames below them, they whooped and waved their guns in the air, as though seeing a hated enemy brought to its knees.

Then the flying machine roared. It wheeled and lowered its head, and the men threw themselves to the ground. Bruno saw a flash; a jet of fire. The earth shook and a mushroom of smoke rose, and then the men were gone and the forest was burning.

Bruno dropped from the tree and ran. He barked and called as Julie and Phillip and Charlie rallied behind him. They had to get away. Humans were slow in the forest. They couldn't climb trees or see properly or use their machines. The chimps had to get out, to run as far as possible, to where the storm couldn't reach them.

They burst into the open, and Bruno skidded to a halt. Ahead of them, the silver wires hummed. Julie screamed and waved her arms. Littleboy ran in circles, howling and pulling out his fur. Stones and branches flew at the fence and bounced off the wires, and then Gido sprang forward. He held a stout branch in one hand, and with it he began to dig at the base of the fence, spraying red earth.

Bruno thumped the ground with his fists. Gido ignored him, ploughing frantically, scrabbling with his hands. Then Bruno ran at him. He shouldered him to the ground and Gido rolled to his feet. He bared his teeth and circled Bruno, who reared up on his back legs and hooted.

Bruno's fur stood on end, puffing him up to twice his size. The other chimps had formed a circle around them now; a wall of yellow teeth, flashing eyes and black fur. He was easily the strongest of all of them, but for a moment something in Bruno wavered.

Just then, there was a whistle. Outside the fence, a cotton tree exploded in a shower of splintered wood and mangled branches, and the circle of chimps broke and scattered into the trees.

The rest of that day, they lay hidden. The pounding and roaring came and went through the forest, and from time to time a human cry would rise in terror or victory. There were no grunts or hoots from the chimps, no slaps or chuckles or barks. Fires rumbled outside, and the jungle was silent.

As they grew listless with hunger, the chimps dozed. Bruno closed his eyes and a memory appeared. He was in the old forest, clutched tightly in his mother's arms. She was running, and as she ran, shapes appeared in the trees on either side. They were chimps; enemies from another valley. A moment later they were up, swinging through the trees, and as Bruno looked down, he saw Gombe turn to fight…

Crack – crack – crack!

He jumped. There were footsteps at the fence, a mutter of voices. Bruno whooped. Bala had come.

Beside the dens, Bala stood with three men. Their clothes were black with dirt, their skin shiny and their eyes rimmed red. Watches and bracelets dangled from their wrists; necklaces hung around their necks. The biggest of them was a ferocious male, taller than Bala. As he spoke, his lip curled and he pushed out his chest. The other man held Bala by the collar, and Bala's voice shook as he gestured to the chimps.

But it was the youngest of the three that Bruno looked at. He was a boy, and although his head barely reached Bala's shoulder, his face seemed familiar. His eyes bulged and he roared and spat and waved his gun. It was this boy that Bala was most afraid of, and he looked at the ground as he spoke to him, eager to submit. The other two were enjoying the show, and they prodded Bala with their guns.

Bruno barked and hurled a stone at them. The men ducked. Then one of them raised his gun. There was a click and slide of metal, and Bala opened his mouth.

"Wait!"

It was the boy. He held up his hand and looked at Bruno, and Bruno bared his teeth. The stare drew out. The jungle shivered. Then the boy's face softened. The rage left his eyes, and he hooted like a chimp. He picked up a rock and made to throw it. He swayed and jumped and chattered. All the time he said the name: *Bruno*. He gestured to his companions as if to make them understand, and as this strange performance went on, the memory of some lost happiness filled him.

Bruno watched. There was no doubt now; he knew this boy. Maybe he had been among the schoolchildren who came to visit, or had once held his mother's hand and pointed to Bruno and Julie when they lived in their cage.

When the boy stopped, the four men were still. Guns crackled in the distance. Bala looked at the ground, and the other two shuffled.

Suddenly, the boy laughed. It was a high, painful laugh. He screwed up his eyes and the others laughed too. They jeered and waved at Bruno and shouldered their rifles, and as they marched off, they cuffed Bala and his cap fell to the ground. For a long time, Bala didn't move. Then he sat down and put his head in his hands.

There was food that evening, and as Bala tossed it through the wires, the chimps caught it and whimpered gratefully. That night, the storm came upon them again. Littleboy whimpered and pulled out his hair. Julie wrapped her arms around him. Above them, the clouds flickered and trees buckled and burned. The air stank of smoke. Men moved back and forth through the jungle like creatures already dead. Sometime before dawn, Littleboy panicked and began to run in circles, and as he passed close to the fence, there was a clap of thunder and he fell to the ground.

In the end, Bruno slept. At dawn, a sound woke him. Down by the stream, frogs sang. In the sky, the mist of the night thinned and vanished. The trees stirred gently and there was a whisper, rising and falling, like the rush of distant water. Bruno shivered and cocked his head as the sound drew close.

He knew then that it was not the thing that had attacked the humans and burned their city. It came from the forest, a voice no human could hear, and as he listened he remembered his mother and his old life. Then the sound stole away, through the fence, and faded among the trees.

It was when he heard the frogs again that he noticed. The guns were silent.

New Beginnings

Even in the heat of dry season, there were places that never burned. Water ran beneath the ground, and when the trees drew it up through their roots, it gathered as mist in the hills and dripped from the leaves. In the sky, clouds bunched and swelled. The flying machines came and went, but when thunder rumbled again, it began to rain: cold, clean rain that quenched the fires and drenched the leaves, and washed away the smoke and blood.

Bala came, and there was a new light in his eyes. He bounded up to Bruno and shouted, "Comb!" Bruno grunted with pleasure and ran his fingers through his fur, as he had done in the old days, and Bala laughed.

There were baby chimps in the nursery and men and women to feed them, and every day new visitors arrived. Congo had returned, sitting in the trees outside the fence, and when Bala saw her, his eyes shone. He did not try to catch her and bring her inside. He hooted gently to her, and for a moment it seemed that he would whoop and run like a chimp.

There was someone else Bala waited for; someone important. Bruno could hear it in his voice and see it in his excited, distracted eyes. He hooted madly at the though of Bala's mysterious new friend, swinging his arms and hurling himself among the ropes and branches like a circus performer. But in the meantime, there was work to be done.

Their first priority was Littleboy. Julie had found him the morning after the storm - curled into a ball at the far end of the enclosure. He rocked back and forth, his teeth bared in a grimace. He had torn out most of his own fur and even begun to chew his fingers. At night he wailed and cried while Julie wrapped her arms around him.

Together, they brought him to the tap and passed him Bruno's plastic bottle. It was a gift from Bala, but Littleboy was allowed to have it, and for a short time his eyes would focus again. He would absorb himself in the bottle, screwing and unscrewing its lid, filling it with water.

Bruno and Julie sat with Littleboy and groomed what was left of his fur. But something inside Littleboy had been broken, and before long he would begin to twitch and pant again, his eyes darting frantically towards the bush.

At last, Bala took him away. Bruno knew that sick chimps were often brought outside, and that when they returned, the sickness was always gone. Wounds had healed. Rashes and boils vanished. Rotten teeth were removed. And so, whenever Littleboy left for the day, Bruno looked towards the clinic and waited.

All the time, more visitors came. There were schoolchildren and white men with cameras; men and women in suits and shining cars.

Once, as a crowd of children waved outside the fence, Bruno saw a face he recognised. A boy, hiding at the back of the group. His shirt was crisp yellow, his hair neatly cut. He was taller than all his friends, and while they whooped and shouted Bruno's name, the boy looked on with a quiet smile. It was the child soldier who had stood at the fence a year before.

Bruno panted and his fur rose, but by the time he had found a stone to throw, the children were moving on, and the boy had vanished.

It was shortly after this that Bala came inside their enclosure. For years Bruno had begged him, longing to hug him properly again. He saw straight away that Bala had changed. The tuft of hair under his cap was smaller and his skin was soft and pulpy like a ripe mango.

Bruno ran his fingers through Bala's hair and beard and carefully cleaned around his eyes. He studied Bala's shoelaces and socks and hugged him. Bala slapped Bruno's back warmly and hooted.

There was a reason that Bala had come inside. A new arrival was ready to join Bruno's group – a chimp unlike any other. Her fur was white and her face was pink, and one eye glowed blue. Her name was Pinkie, and when Phillip and Charlie saw her, they shuffled uncertainly. She barely looked like a chimp.

Julie reached for her eagerly, and Bala let her run her fingers through Pinkie's fur. But when Pinkie refused to play, Julie sulked and threw stones. Bala scolded her, and then Bruno plunged among them. He threw the younger chimps aside and reared on his back legs, beating the earth with his fists. It wasn't long before the chimps accepted Pinkie, and she learned her place.

The rains were drawing to an end when Bala's long-awaited visitor came. Julie heard them first. and gave a bark of joy. Bruno smelled the sweet smell of flowers and milk, and he jumped up and down and spun where he stood.

They met Sharmila at the den. Bala stood proudly beside her. In her arms she held a fat naked creature, no bigger than a young chimp. Sharmila smiled and touched it constantly, and when she pointed to Bruno and said his name, the creature flapped its arms and gurgled.

Bruno pressed against the bars. He reached out a hand, straining until he could stroke this strange, delicate thing. A human. A newborn human, with wisps of fur on its head and rolls of fat under its chin. Bruno reached out to take it, but this time Sharmila pulled back. A strange ache filled him. He paced about, and when Bala lifted his baby son into his arms, his face changed in a way that Bruno had never seen.

A cry interrupted them. It was Phillip, and at the sound of his voice, Julie barked and her fur rose. Bala placed his son back in Sharmila's arms. At the other end of the enclosure, people were shouting. Littleboy had fallen, and would not get up.

That evening, they waited. The chatter of late afternoon had stopped, and through the twilight came low, sad voices as the humans talked amongst themselves. Then the lights of the buildings were switched off. The chimps wandered into their dens, and as the humans departed for the night, Julie walked in circles, sniffing the air and calling to Littleboy. Once they were inside, she lowered her head. Bruno hugged her. Littleboy was gone, and while the humans slept in their beds and the chimps dozed in each other's arms, Bruno and Julie cried quietly for their lost friend.

The Second Son

At first, he was just like a chimp. Sharmila carried him in her arms, just as she had once carried Bruno, and he gurgled and cried and clamoured for attention. But as he grew, Bruno saw that he was different.

He was slower than a chimp, and he did not bite or climb or cling to Sharmila's back. By his third year, the sounds he made had become sharp and clear, and he soon joined in with the chattering of his parents.

Their visits were rare, and however much Bruno begged, they would not come inside the enclosures to play. Each time Sharmila and her son appeared, Bruno would notice a change – the thick dark hair on the child's head; the white trainers on his feet as he grew big enough to run around on his own. And with each change, Bruno saw a reminder of his old life. He knew that this child now sat with Bala in front of the TV and ate his food and slept in a bed.

With every month, new chimps arrived. There were other enclosures now, other leaders, and Bruno heard their calls during the day. There was Gorilla; a powerful male and the closest in size to Bruno, followed by Mama Lucy. Behind these strong

62

and clever chimps were gangs of youngsters, and as each group came to maturity, the biggest among them swaggered and competed for dominance.

All the chimps knew about Congo. She was a constant visitor, and Bruno could tell when she had arrived by the chorus of greeting calls. For months she vanished, and when she returned she held one arm curled against her chest, as though shielding something precious. At the sight of her, every chimp in the sanctuary ran to the edge of its cage, reaching and straining and screaming in excitement. Tucked against her, thin and bright-eyed, was a newborn baby chimp.

At night, safe behind the walls of the den, Bruno dreamed. They were in the forest, in the time he barely remembered, and all around them, bodies swung through the canopy. They came to a place where the trees ended and the ground fell, and the vast space and blaze of the sun made his fur tingle.

Gombe looked to the clouds and the flickering sky, and he reared on his back legs and swayed. He swung a branch and bared his teeth. Then he dropped and pounded the earth with his fists. As he whooped, the sky above them exploded and rain slashed down.

Through his mother's fur, Bruno watched. The voice in the forest was loud now. It was the thing that Gombe cried out to, that made the clouds rumble and the rain fall, and only in the dark could you hear its great heart beating…

He woke to the sound of a fly. It buzzed among the concrete walls, and there was a hiss and splash as someone mopped the floors of the next den. Outside, the other chimps called for their breakfast. The men who fed them watched and chattered, and there was a screech as two younger chimps bickered over a chunk of pineapple until Julie intervened.

Bruno went out, collected his meal, and sat down. When he had eaten his banana, he rolled the skin into a pulpy wad and pressed it between his lips, sucking the juice out of it.

Beyond the wires stood buckets of fresh fruit, and he wished he could step outside just long enough to grab one. The men babbled. They were talking about Gido, saying his name and pointing. Bruno spat out the banana skin and turned.

He had seen Gido the previous night, hooting and displaying to Congo on the other side of the fence. Now he was missing. Bruno's fur rose. Then Phillip chuckled. He had two portions of food. There was spare food in the men's buckets, and as they raised their voices, Charlie barked. He was staring at the gate in the fence.

It was open. It had been opened from the inside, and a broken padlock and a broken branch lay in the grass beside it. An odd stillness fell, as though no-one could believe what was happening. Then, with a shriek of delight, Charlie ran to the open gate and burst through. Bruno froze. Charlie raced towards the buckets of food, and as they saw him coming, the two men opened their mouths and fled. With a grunt, Bruno dashed straight after Charlie.

As soon as he was in the open, Bruno spun in panic. Charlie scampered ahead, enthralled by the toys and buildings. Julie barked as she followed Bruno through the gate, Phillip behind her.

In an instant, there was chaos. Buckets and mops clattered to the ground as men dropped them. Bruno barked and hooted; chimps spilled through the gate into the open. They were outside. An unknown place. There were no silver wires, nothing to protect them, and as they understood this, the chimps bristled in terror. The humans fled and Bruno called to them to come back. Then he hurried among the buildings.

He knew only two things: he had to find Bala, and he had to protect the other chimps from danger. Where the buildings ended, there stood a set of gates. Beside these stood the old cages where he had once lived with Julie. Beyond the gates lay a steep road and, shimmering in the trees, the lake that Bruno had first seen so many years before.

From the road ahead came a rumble. A car. It appeared among the trees, and as the people inside saw Bruno, there was a flurry of excitement. A pair of white men leaned out of the windows and began to flash their cameras. The driver of the car looked uneasy.

Bruno bared his teeth. *No.* They were strangers. He picked up a stone and began to sway. The driver was shaking his head now, shouting and pointing to Bruno, but the white men didn't care; grinning as they raised their cameras. As their teeth flashed, Bruno's chest grew tight. He reared up, swung his arms, screamed. Behind him, dimly, he heard Julie cry out. One of the men flinched and turned, but it was too late, the car was still coming. With a bellow, Bruno charged.

He struck the car with his shoulder and beat and pounded with his fists. A piece of metal tore loose. At the sight of this, a triumphant rage swept through him. The car lurched forward, its weight closing down on him. Bruno's feet scrabbled. He howled and smashed a window, and when a hand came within reach, he sank his teeth into it. Then he was free.

The car swerved. It ploughed into the gate and a moment later the men were out and running. The injured one clutched his hand to his chest. Bruno chased them for a short distance, but he could see that they were frightened. He turned back.

Only then did Bruno see the driver. He had picked up a stout stick and he was running back up the road. Back into the sanctuary.

From the gates came a bark, as Julie saw the man. He came out of the forest; a tall stranger with a black stick. In a moment, they knew, he would raise it. He would point it at them and there would be a puff of smoke and a crack like two stones smashing together.

Julie cried out, and as the man skidded to a halt, the other chimps joined her. For a moment, he was the first human they had ever seen; the one they had known before Bala and the fences and food; the man who had killed their mothers and taken them away.

Then Phillip charged. He bared his teeth, his fur standing on end. The others were behind him. There was a flurry of blows, the cry of a human voice. The air trembled. Then silence.

Bruno came to the gate and stopped. The chimps had scattered, and they huddled in the trees now and whimpered. In the centre of the clearing, the man lay face down. Bruno walked over to look at him. The fighting was over. He had submitted.

Bruno groomed him and waited for him to get up. Blood soaked through the man's clothes and stained the earth. Human skin was so soft. Bruno poked the figure and grunted, but the man did not move. The forest seemed to hold its breath, and Julie watched him from the trees with wide, frightened eyes.

Something cold and heavy reached into Bruno's chest

and squeezed him. The man was hurt. Bruno coughed and blinked. Bala would be angry.

From the road, there was a crack of gunfire. The chimps scattered into the bush. Three strangers appeared, two of them with guns, and they ran to help the fallen man. When they rolled him over, his body was limp, and as they looked at him their faces went hard.

The chimps whimpered and glanced hopefully at the gates of the sanctuary. But Bruno pulled away. Bala could not see them. Not after this.

He looked up at the hills, dark and lonely and alive with sounds. Julie and Phillip watched him expectantly. Then Bruno turned his back on the sanctuary, and plunged into the forest.

The Wild

The rains had ended. Rivers ran full, and the forest hummed with life. Great trunks of mahogany reached into the sky. Duiker and antelope skipped through the undergrowth. A civet cat watched from the trees and, higher up, colobus monkeys bounced and chattered. Streams churned and splashed across slippery boulders, and in the swamps turtles and crocodiles blinked and vanished beneath the water. This was the old forest, where nothing had yet been chopped or burned; where life twitched and heaved in a tangle of green shoots and muddy red earth.

Bruno bristled with fear. His heart pounded, and he longed for the comfort of fences and men with food. Behind him, the rest of the chimps milled uncertainly.

In total, thirty-one had escaped. Many had fled at the sound of gunshots and become lost in the forest. Others had found themselves back in the sanctuary and were quickly captured as humans fanned out to search for them. But most had followed their leader.

They had barely stopped for water. Bala was behind them somewhere, scouring the forest. Now and then, they heard a human voice or caught the scent of rice or meat or groves of mangoes, and Phillip and Charlie swayed hungrily. But Bruno barked and drove them back. Bala could not find them.

On the third day, Julie stopped. She glanced back towards the sanctuary and gave a nervous hoot. The younger chimps could not go on eating leaves and the odd lizard, and she no longer had the strength to carry them. She approached Bruno and groomed him. Then, cautiously, she shuffled back the way she had come.

With a howl, Bruno knocked Julie down. She rolled and screamed, but when she found her feet she galloped to a safe distance and looked at him. Bruno rose on his back legs and swung his arms. He stuck out his chin and gibbered and grunted. He was seething. But when he picked up a branch and began to sway, Julie did not submit. She hooted softly, like a young chimp pleading with an angry parent.

Then Charlie rose and went to her side. Phillip followed a second later, then Christo and Tito. They gathered around Julie, and when Bruno barked and refused to join them, they turned at last and disappeared into the forest.

That night, he tried to build a nest. It was hopeless. The branches snapped or came apart when he took his hand away. In the distance, the city twinkled, and at dawn a cry woke him as another of the escaped chimps was captured. The traps were easy to spot. Bruno had spent enough time with humans to know the smell of soap and cigarette smoke. He could tell by the taste of water in a stream whether a village lay up-current. Wherever humans passed, the trees had been felled and carried away, and in these places the earth was parched and dusty. And so Bruno moved deeper into the forest, where streams flowed and boughs hung heavy with banana and mango.

He was picking his way down the banks of a river when a shriek rose from the forest ahead and there was a crash of branches. It was Gido.

Bruno had not seen him since they left the sanctuary. He was screaming now, fighting something among the trees, and there came a snap and thump as he swung on a branch. Bruno ran. He could not see Gido, but as he neared the source of the sound, there was a final death-cry and a raw chant of victory. Then the attack came.

They dropped from the branches; black shapes with yellow fangs, and in an instant they were upon him. A set of teeth sank into his shoulder. Hands fumbled to pin him down. Fingers dug into him, and Bruno squirmed and screamed for Bala. The stink of their breath was everywhere and they began to beat with their fists, raining blows on his body. *No.* Bruno thrashed. He was frightened now in a way he had never been before, and as he felt the air driven from his lungs, he pulled hopelessly to free himself.

For a moment, their grip faltered. Bruno raised his arm. Then, with a bellow, he pulled free and threw one of the wild chimps against the others. They rolled on the ground in a chaos of snarls, and then Bruno was up.

He reached a fallen tree just as the wild chimps rushed him again, and knocked the first of them into the river below. He would beat them. He was alive; teeth bared, fur on end, eyes blazing. He stamped on the trunk and swayed; the rhythm caught and held, and when he beat his fists and tore up a branch, the sky burst. Rain slashed down, and Bruno shook himself in a spray of mist and blood.

The chimps fell back. The rain steadied to a patter, and Bruno sat to inspect his wounded shoulder. The chimps looked at each other and coughed. Then one of them crept forward and began to groom him. The rain dwindled, and as it dripped through the trees, the wild chimps gathered around this enormous stranger.

They had barely settled when there was a sound of footsteps. They raised their heads, and with a short cry of alarm, they vanished. Bruno looked around. He was alone, as if nothing had happened. From the trees came a crackle as bodies stumbled about. He hid.

"Bruno!"

Something lurched inside him. The trees rustled. Then, one by one, they appeared.

They were like a group of chimps, walking on their back legs. Their hands were empty, with no guns or sticks, and they called Bruno's name.

Leading them was Bala. He did not shout or scold or wave his arms. He picked his way among the trees with hardly a sound, and when he looked up at the sun falling through the canopy, Bruno saw that he was at peace.

When they had passed, Bruno trembled. Then he turned toward the sanctuary, and ran. As he went he hooted and crashed and called out to the whole world, and by the time he reached the gates, it was evening. Somewhere ahead, Charlie and Phillip chuckled to each other as their dinner arrived.

She was waiting for him where the trees ended. At her feet, her baby rolled in the grass, and when she saw Bruno, she stumbled towards him. Congo did not stop her. The baby tugged at Bruno's fur and he patted her gently. In front of them, the sanctuary was still. The young chimps had just been fed. The fences hummed, holding back the forest. In the dim light, Bruno picked out Phillip and Charlie, sitting in their enclosure. Julie was building a nest. None of them had been harmed.

Slowly, like water draining from a pool, the heavy feeling left Bruno's chest. From the nursery came a whimper as a baby chimp squirmed and shivered, searching for the thump of its mother's heart. Then a pair of hands picked it up and cuddled it.

A voice spoke; soft and soothing as a breeze in dry grass, and as he heard it, Bruno was filled with sudden warmth. He stepped forward, towards Bala and his old life. Then he saw them.

They hung in the trees around him; wild chimps of all ages, and he knew then that they were waiting. The voice in the forest whispered to him and the whisper rose to a song, a deep chant that swayed in his ears and would not let him go. It was the sound of the lost world, of water in deep caves, and ancient trees creaking at dawn. It was everything his mother had known and taught him, passed down from their ancestors in ways that no-one can understand, and as he heard it, he knew it was the call of home.

Down in the sanctuary, the lights began to switch off. Bala had just got into his car when a chorus of hooting rose from the chimps in their cages. His eyes searched the trees, but it was growing dark.

From the edge of the forest, Bruno watched. He coughed, and although he was not afraid, he trembled. Every fibre of his body urged him forward, towards the man who loved him and the life he had known for nearly twenty years.

But instead, he stopped. He lowered his head and turned towards the forest. And then he was gone.

From left to right: Julie, Bala, Sharmila and Bruno in 1991

Afterword

From the moment my wife and I met him in 1989, Bruno became a member of our family, and changed our lives. From the founding of the Tacuguma Chimpanzee Sanctuary in 1995 to his escape in 2006 and in the years since then, he has continued to be my inspiration. It was Bruno who taught me about chimpanzees, Bruno who showed me the need to respect our environment and to co-exist peacefully with other species.

Bruno's escape in 2006 was a rare and tragic accident. Melvin Mammah, a Sierra Leonean on a visit to the sanctuary, lost three fingers to Bruno. His companion, Issa Kanu, lost his life to the rest of the chimps. The incident highlights the respect we must show to these intelligent and powerful animals. Melvin has since become a friend of the sanctuary and holds no ill-will towards chimpanzees - his one regret is that he has not had the chance to make peace with Bruno himself.

After the escape, I was heartbroken - the relationship I had with Bruno was no different from that of a father and son. But once again Bruno was showing us the way. Chimpanzees need more than a sanctuary, they need to be protected in the wild, along with the forest they live in.

Whether we see Bruno again, whether he is captured or killed, or whether he will live out his life in his natural home, depends entirely on us humans. Every year more forests are cleared and chimpanzee habitats continue to shrink. At Tacugama our focus has broadened: from rescuing chimps to educating young people. We work with communities, conduct conservation research and lobby the government to protect Sierra Leone's forests and wild places.

Bruno changed my life and the lives of many others. I am thankful to Paul for his dedication to Bruno's story, and for creating a book that speaks directly to my heart. I am sure it will speak to you too, and change the way you look at our closest living relative, the chimpanzee. They have much more to show us, and to teach us about ourselves.

Bala Amarasekaran
Tacugama Chimpanzee Sanctuary, 2013

The Author

Paul Glynn is an Irish artist, writer and award-winning documentary filmmaker. He became captivated by Bruno's story following the chimp's escape in 2006 and has been a friend of the Tacugama Chimpanzee Sanctuary ever since. He currently lives in London.

 @theyoungerearth

Learn more

www.tacugama.com